Books by Lindsay MacRae

HOW TO AVOID KISSING YOUR
PARENTS IN PUBLIC

HOW TO MAKE A SNAIL FALL
IN LOVE WITH YOU

YOU CANNY SHOVE YER GRANNY OFF A BUS!

Lindsay MacRae

How to Make a Snail Fall in Love with You

and Other Surprising Poems

Illustrated by Steven Appleby

PUFFIN

PUFFIN BOOKS

Published by the Penguin Group
Penguin Books Ltd, 80 Strand, London WC2R 0RL, England
Penguin Putnam Inc., 375 Hudson Street, New York, New York 10014, USA
Penguin Books Australia Ltd, 250 Camberwell Road, Camberwell, Victoria 3124, Australia
Penguin Books Canada Ltd, 10 Alcorn Avenue, Toronto, Ontario, Canada M4V 3B2
Penguin Books India (P) Ltd, 11 Community Centre, Panchsheel Park, New Delhi – 110 017, India
Penguin Books (NZ) Ltd, Cnr Rosedale and Airborne Roads, Albany, Auckland, New Zealand
Penguin Books (South Africa) (Pty) Ltd, 24 Sturdee Avenue, Rosebank 2196, South Africa

Penguin Books Ltd, Registered Offices: 80 Strand, London WC2R 0RL, England

www.penguin.com

First published 2003
1

Set in Baskerville MT

Made and printed in England by Clays Ltd, St Ives plc

British Library Cataloguing in Publication Data
A CIP catalogue record for this book is available from the British Library

ISBN 0-141-31430-3

For Francis, Kitty and Angus

Contents

Embarrassing Rap

Your shirt's too tight
It looks brand new
You're forty, Dad
Not twenty-two
You're a sight, man
Look at the state of you

AND STOP EMBARRASSING ME!

Your laugh sounds like
You've choked on toast
Were you sent that haircut
Through the post?
I beg the Father, Son and Holy Ghost

THAT YOU'LL STOP EMBARRASSING ME!

You're the 'Look' what got dragged in
By the cat
You've taken up running
Cos you're running to fat
But do you really have
To wear shorts like that?

THEY'RE BOUND TO EMBARRASS ME!

Dad, get a grip
And get a hold
Accept the fact you're getting old
And do exactly as you're told

STOP EMBARRASSING ME!

You Are What's in Your Pockets

What are little boys made of?

One blunt pencil, badly chewed;
A battery you always lose
But which then turns up again;
Grit, fluff, someone else's pen.
Matter that once filled your nose
Or lived in between your toes –
Whatever it is,
It's green and glows:
That's what boys are made of.

What are little girls made of?

Scrunched-up tissues, old hair clips,
Some foul-tasting gloop for lips;
Notes which say: 'YOU'RE NOT MY FRIEND!';
Grit, fluff, someone else's pen;
Sticky, purple glittery stuff
Of which you can never have enough;
Chocolate –
For when the going gets tough:
That's what girls are made of.

A Convent of Nouns

A pack of suitcases
A herd of sounds
A flock of wallpaper
A deck of chairs
A litter of sweet wrappers
A shoal of naked swimmers
A swarm of summers
A set of French sevens
A brace of dentists
A round of wheels
A pot of bellies
A peel of oranges
A nough of this poem

The Unchosen One

Sally never gets picked
or gets picked on.
When she's bad her name's
not on the board.
If she puts her hand up in the classroom
and waves it about, it's ignored.
She's deselected
        unelected
Even her nits go uninspected.
If she has an idea
it gets rejected.
She's overlooked
        not booked
        passed over
        kicked into touch.
When someone says, 'What'll you give me for Sally?'
Someone else answers,
'Not much!'
She's never one of the many chosen
or one of the chosen few.
And only when it's 'Do It Yourself'
does Sally get anything to do.
It's always 'Don't Ring Us
We'll Ring You.'
But Sally doesn't let it bother her
She prefers
        elects
        chooses
        selects
not to.

A Wristwatch Whines

You look at me twenty times a day
But you never say hello
You wind me up
But you never apologize
If you're late
You say I'm running slow
If you're too early
Then I'm fast
You should not get me wet
But you forget
You shake me in fury
You say that I'm not working
As though I'm lazy
When I'm simply heartbroken.

The Seven Deadly E-mails

Pride *n.*   *the state of feeling or being proud, too great self-esteem, a proper sense of what is becoming to oneself and scorn of what is unworthy.*

To: J. K. Rowling

From: P. Ride

Subject: A Few Helpful Hints

I have much enjoyed your Harry Potter books.
I am very good myself at writing stories.
I know I did very well in my SATs test.
So I hope you won't mind if I suggest a few improvements:

1. I don't know anyone with glasses called Harry. There's a boy in my class called Damilola who is quite short-sighted so perhaps you could call Harry Damilola instead – it would make it more realistic.

2. Also – what kind of name is Hagrid?
   Maybe you're not that great at spelling and really
   meant to write Haggard (as in when you've stayed up
   past your bedtime and don't look too hot in the
   morning).
   It's kinda ironic that someone who writes about magic
   and wizards can't spell, isn't it?
   Geddit? Spelling – wizards? *Spelling – wizards!*

3. I have tried aiming a luggage trolley just over halfway
   between platforms nine and ten at King's Cross
   station and I GOT TOLD OFF!!!!
   Also, I could have hurt myself. Don't you think you're
   being a bit irresponsible?

4. Quite honestly the books are a bit long.
   I myself never write a story which is more than one
   page and I *still* get a good mark.
   Perhaps you should try it!!!

Ten Times Tables

Please, miss
Can I move tables?
I don't like it here by the door
And I don't want to sit next to Jasmine
She's not my best friend any more.

Please, miss
Can I move tables?
The boys all make faces at me
They were ugly enough in Reception
But they're uglier still in Year 3.

Please, miss
Can I move tables?
Charlie keeps stealing my pen
Alexandra's forgotten her rubber
And is borrowing mine – yet again!

Please, miss
Can I move tables?
You can smell the school dinners from here
The reek of old sprouts and fish fingers
Has made me come over all queer.

Please, miss
Can I move tables?
Philip Grimlet is picking his nose
Then smearing the snot on his book bag
Or flicking it on to our clothes.

Please, miss
Can I move tables?
I feel really sick and I worry
That if it gets very much worse, miss
I might need the bin in a hurry.

Please, miss
Can I move tables?
Victoria Glimp has got nits
Though *that* really isn't the problem
I just don't like the way that she sits.

Please, miss
Can I move tables?
The sun's shining right in my eyes
Plus I can't stand the snivelling noises
Victoria makes when she cries.

Please, miss
Can I move tables?
This lot support M.U.F.C.
And they said lots of really rude words, miss
When I said I support Coventry.

Yes, dear
You **can** move tables
While you're at it move **country** as well
Move as **far** as you can from my
classroom
There's no need to wait for the bell!

The Giggles

Hee hee
hee hee
hee!

Alexandra Daunton-Diggle
Was swallowed by a giant giggle
Which started gently at her toes
And finished just above her nose

No one saw, no one heard
It came and went without a word
Gobbling her whole (plus party frock)
It spat out one white cotton sock

All sniggerers should have a care
That giggles take you unawares
And that no matter what you do
They always get the better of you

Middle Child

The piggy in the middle
The land between sky and sea
The cheese which fills the sandwich
The odd one out of three
The one who gets the hand-me-downs
And broken bits of junk
The follower, not the leader
The one in the bottom bunk

The one for whom the pressure's off
The one who can run wild
The one who holds the balance of power
The lucky second child

It's MY turn to be in the middle!

No, MINE!

The Fallout

I hate Emily Becker
and Emily hates me.
We haven't talked since morning play
and now it's half-past three.
I think her hair looks stupid,
she drives me round the bend,
I can't believe that yesterday
she was my bestest friend.
She's thrown me back my pencil case
I've chucked her back her pen,
we loathe each other's guts so much
I doubt we'll speak again.

Now it is tomorrow,
we've both forgotten why
we're not talking to each other
when Emily says 'Hi'.
I give her back my pencil case.
She swaps it for the pen.
It's peace, not war,
best mates once more
then we fall out again.

I hate Emily Becker
and Emily hates me.
Our hatred is the only thing
on which we can agree.
She's a big-headed show-off
who thinks she's really great.
I can't believe that yesterday
she was my special mate.
But I'll let her keep my pencil case
and I'll hang on to her pen
cos although we fall out all the time
we always fall in again.

Names on a Bench

On many of the park benches on Hampstead Heath in London there are names of people who have died. Relatives of the dead often sponsor benches as a memorial to their loved ones.

The empty park is full of people –
Invisible married couples
With no second names:
Ted and Mary
Frank and Isobel
Shirley and Jack.
All that we know about them,
From the small gold plaque, is that
'They loved each other' and
'They loved this place'.

Up on the hill
More names are carved
Into wood and painted black
By someone working for the council
Rather than by a penknife for a dare or laugh.
They sound like a teenage gang:
Jaman, Paul, Kerry, Clare
And a younger Jack.
Their dates of birth and death
Show that they never left
Their awkward teens behind
For long enough
To find long-lasting love.

Down by the open gate
Lie flowers and a sodden teddy bear,
A fading sign hung round its broken neck:
'We'll miss you always
        Sweet dreams.
            Mum and Dad X'

The tired driver
Speeding home from work
Saw him too late –
A tiny restless blur,
Too young to stop
Or think
Or wait.

Soon he'll have a bench
Which overlooks the swings and roundabouts.
His parents will come to sit
And listen to the noisy laughter
Of other children.
With sore tears drying on their cheeks,
They'll imagine the wonderful life
He didn't live to have.
And how, in a perfect world,
It ought to be the children, not the parents
Who order the bench, the black letters
Or the golden plaque.

The Seven Deadly E-mails

Wrath *n.*   *violent anger, an instance, or fit, of this: holy indignation.*

To: Whom It May Concern

From: W. Rath

Subject: Bone Picking

Let me just say

I am not pleased
I am not at all pleased
I have never been less pleased in my whole life
A life which
is **not** coming up roses
Which
is **not** even coming up daffodils
Which
is coming up **weeds**
I am angry, cross, livid
Hopping mad
Absolutely furious
Fuming, on the warpath
Smoke is coming out of my ears
Flames are shooting from my nostrils
I am well miffed, not a happy bunny
Unimpressed
Vexed

Hot under the collar
On edge
In a huff
In a temper
I'm seriously annoyed
I've got a cob on (whatever that is)
And it **doesn't** suit me
I've got the hump
But I **didn't** order it!
I need to let off steam
I'm going to scream
I'm irate
Got too much on my plate
I'm infuriated, irritated,
Incensed, inflamed, exasperated
Anything which gets in my way
Is liable to be
ANNIHILATED
I'm beyond reason
It's open season
On everything and everyone
There's just no pleasing
me
SO DON'T EVEN THINK ABOUT IT
I am
IN-CAN-DES-CENT
with RAGE !!!!!!!!!!

Right,
Now I've got that off my chest ...

You Tell Me

You explain that all men are born equal
You say I should never tell lies
You teach me that sunlight and rain
        make the crops grow
Not bullets and bombs from the skies
You whisper that I shouldn't worry
You're a grown-up
        while I am still young
You beg me, don't fight with my brother
Then tell me that war has begun

The Only One Smiling

The only one smiling
is the one who hasn't heard the latest news.

The only one not crying
is the one who has nothing left
(not even hope)
to lose.

Hate Is

Hate knows only half the story,
Hate sees half the view,
Hate does things you didn't mean to do.

Hate can poison all your life
Or simply ruin your day,
Hate says things you didn't mean to say.

Hate can turn your heart to stone
And turn your voice to steel.
Hate takes all the good things that you feel,

Turns them into dust and ashes,
Makes the truth a lie,
Hate's too busy growing to ask why.

Hate will make your friend your enemy,
Hate will start a war.
Is hate something that's worth dying for?

Love Is

Love can make your heart beat faster.
Love can make you shake.
Love is worse than chickenpox or stomach-ache.

Love can make the ugly handsome,
Make the nerdy cool.
Love can turn the brightest person into a gibbering fool.

Love makes you forget your homework.
Love makes you lose your place.
Love's like a frozen haddock in the face,

Sure to leave you feeling shocked
And looking like a prat.
Love's a bit ... like that!

LOVE-TINTED
SPECTACLES

Who? ME?!

Divorce: A Spell to Prevent It

If I avoid the lines and cracks
Between the paving stones;
If I leap from the small dark island
Left by a recent shower
To the safe shore of its neighbouring continent,
                  Then it won't happen.

If I leave nothing on my plate;
If I find each lost toy
And every stray piece of paper;
If I behave with no more emotion
Than the clothes I wear;
If, like them, I lurk in cupboards,
Silent and out of the way –
                  Then it won't happen.

If *I* say that I'm sorry;
If *I* take the blame;
If I tell them it's *my* fault;
If I pray and pray
And give up chocolate,
                  Then it won't happen.

If I could just invent a joke
Which will make them both laugh
                    Perhaps it won't happen.

If I ignore it
              it won't happen
If I try harder
              it won't happen
If I am perfect
              it won't happen.

Oops!

The Seven Deadly E-mails

Envy *n.*   *an extreme feeling of annoyance at the good looks, qualities, fortune, etc., of another.*

To: The Blue-Eyed Monster

From: N.V. (The Green-Eyed Monster)

Subject: The Red-Eyed Monster

Don't you just **hate** the way
she can get two whole children in her mouth at once
and swallow them
without spitting out the bones?

Or the way
she leaves extra-thick, snot-green slime
wherever she roams –
The so-thick-it's-almost-solid kind
which takes all eternity to get off?

OK, so the whole of Europe is
terrified of her.
So what!
I made quite an impact
on New Zealand
in my time.

But what annoys me most
are her huge red eyes.
She reckons they look
like bottomless cauldrons of blood
and that they're scarier
than green
or blue ones.
As if!

I reckon
I could
fit
MORE
children
in.

Why I Don't Need
to Do My Homework

Gonna be gorgeous, gonna be seen
Always on the cover of a magazine
Gonna only travel in a limousine

COS I JUST WANNA BE FAMOUS

Gonna eat chips with pink champagne
Make sure everyone knows my name
Gonna have my picture in the Hall of Fame

ALL BECAUSE I'LL BE FAMOUS

Gonna wear more jewellery than the Queen and the
Pope
Never gonna brush my teeth or wash my neck with soap
Gonna have an entourage instead of friends, I hope

WHEN I GET TO BE FAMOUS

Gonna get my famous foot in every famous door
Gonna make some serious cash then seriously make
 some more
Now all I need to worry about is what I'll be famous *for*

THOUGH I'M SURE I'M GONNA BE
ALMOST
CERTAINLY
I JUST WANNA BE
FAMOUS!

Beware of the Sheep

It's not very glamorous being a sheep,
We're what people count on to send them to sleep.
A thing which gets shorn and made into a sweater;
That blur in the field getting wetter and wetter.
Part of the landscape, one of the flock,
Who nibbles the grass between boulder and rock.
I lurk on the mountainside shrouded by fog;
Get dipped by a shepherd or chased by his dog.
When a rambler is rambling, safe distance he'll keep
From a horse or a bullock, but never a sheep.
Yet whenever I feel I'm being laughed at or pitied
I'll baa at the person to 'Go and get knitted!'

A GLAMOROUS SHEEP.

SEQUINNED WOOL.

FALSE EYELASHES.

MAKE-UP.

LIPPY.

THIGH-HIGH SHORT FLEECE.

How to Hurt a Cat's Feelings

Sit on it
Call it Rover
Throw sticks for it
Feed it jam sandwiches
Say things like:
> 'Look at you!
> Lounging around all day
> Doing nothing.'

Complain about its breath
Tell it to get a move on when it's using the litter tray
Talk to it in an ickle-wickle voice
the way old ladies talk to babies
Make it watch *Lassie Come Home* on TV
Buy it a power drill for its birthday
Beat it at cards.

Excellent Excuses for Not Tidying Your Room

1. It's *not* a bedroom, it's an ecosystem.

2. The carpet won't wear out so quickly if I cover it with clothes.

3. You should be proud of me. I'm growing our own penicillin.

4. I asked the spiders to spin you something really special for your birthday.

5. YOU JUST DON'T UNDERSTAND!

6. The monster under the bed might finally find its way out.

7. It's a modern art exhibition.

8. You can't just order a bedroom around, you know. ROOMS HAVE RIGHTS TOO!

9. I did it last year.

Problem Child No. 1: Tracey

Tracey is spoilt.

She was left out in the rain too long
and she shrank.

Problem Child No. 2: Ben

Ben is a show-off.

He's always cancelling
trips to the theatre.

Problem Child No. 3: Jane

Jane is a liar.

She's been in bed
for two whole weeks.

Problem Child No. 4: Carol

Carol is a goody-goody.

She's always repeating herself.

Problem Child No. 5: Arabella

Arabella is having a bad hair day.

She had a bad Thursday too.

NAUGHTY
hair!
BAD
hair!

Problem Child No. 6: Stewart

Stewart is a bit dim.

Someone should put
a brighter bulb in him.

Problem Child No. 7: Phillip

Phillip is *so* full of himself.

He hasn't got any room
for his dinner.

Catastrophe

I don't like people much.
Don't like to look them in the eye;
don't like the way they rub
you up the wrong way
and complain about your hair
and fleas and fluff.
Or how, just as you've settled down
upon their lap,
they're off
to get a biscuit or a cup of tea.
(Humans eat too much.)

Worst of the lot are
rough little girls
who dress you up in baby clothes
then shove
you in a pram
and make stupid cooing noises
at you and try to feed you mashed banana –
yuck!

So leave me alone.
                Lay off!
                Buzz off!
                Get lost!
I like it here behind the fridge.
It's warm,
there's crumbs to nibble
and a friendly, soothing hum.

Don't try to poke me out,
rattle the biscuit tin
or shine a torch.

And don't humiliate yourself by screeching
'Here kitty, kitty, kitty, kitty, kitty cat.'
You sound like a cornered mouse
and anyway my proper hunting name is
Selene – Goddess of the Moon.

I will come out
                in my own good time,
                when I feel like it,
                under my own terms,
                when you've gone out.
I have my pride.
I can't be bribed
Though you might try a plate of pilchards in tomato
sauce with some smoked salmon pâté on the side.

The Seven Deadly E-mails

Lust *n.*   *longing, eagerness to possess, to desire eagerly, sexual desire of a degraded kind.*

To: Anyone with One or More of the Following:

Long blonde hair / rippling muscles / fantastic legs / perfect skin with no spots / a gorgeous figure / loads of money / a private island in the Caribbean / a sports car / the latest designer clothes / a yacht / kissable lips / a deep sexy voice / all their own teeth.

From: Someone who's desperate for the above

Subject: Aid Urgently Required

Message: HELP ME, I'M LUST!!!!

A Few of My Least Favourite Things

Polo-neck jumpers and pink fluffy slippers

Smelly old fish, but especially kippers

Friends who are out when you give them a ring
These are a few of my least favourite things

(Oom pah pah – oom pah pah – oom pah pah –
oom pah pah)

Bald, winking uncles who don't send you money

Jokes which your dad tells which aren't at all funny

Riding a bike with your arm in a sling

These are a few of my least favourite things

(Oom pah pah – oom pah pah – oom pah pah –
oom pah pah)

Teachers who spray you with drops of saliva

Timothy Tubbs who still owes me a fiver

All tone-deaf people who think they can sing

These are a few of my least favourite thiiiings

When it's Christmas
Or my birthday
And I'm feeling glad
I simply remember my least favourite things
And then I feel really
BAD.

(Repeat until thoroughly miserable)

Fart from the Madding Crowd

Who expostulated lately?
Who crawled out of their shell?
Who let a ripper
Which stinks like a kipper
Out of the jaws of hell?
Who squeezed a sneaker?
Who leaked a leaker?
Who's looking guilty as well?
Someone please own up
Behave like a grown-up.
Who made that horrible smell?

Wouldn't It Be Luvverly?

All Mum wants is a day in bed
House all tidy and kids all fed
Ten hours of sleep instead
Of doing a pile of ironing.

A prince to bring her a single rose
Who will massage her aching toes
Then lead her to suppose
He'll stay and do the ironing.

He will press everything, including socks
Fold up each shirt
He'll smooth sheets and put the pleats
Back into my old school skirt.

But he fades like a cloud of steam
Mum wakes up with a dreadful scream
It's all been just a dream
There's *still* a pile of ironing
                              ironing
                                    ironing
                                          ironing
                                                i-ron-ing!

The Seven Deadly E-mails

Gluttony *n.*   *excess in eating.*

To: Mr Kipling

From: G. Luttony

Subject: Leftovers

You do bake exceedingly good cakes
I really like the Viennese Fancies
Although the Mini Choco Rolls are delicious too!
My mum only bakes about three cakes a year
which are rock cakes
so you beat her by a long way!
I was just wondering what you do
with the dirty wooden spoons and bowls?
I'm sure that your bakers are very busy
and as they're grown-ups
are probably on diets, etc.
So I was wondering if you would like some help
licking out the bowls and other stuff?
I'm usually free during half-term,
other holidays and at weekends
but *not* Saturday afternoons cos my mum
takes me out for a burger which I wouldn't want to miss.
Please let me know a.s.a.p.
when I can come round to help.

Miss Gray's Lament

I'd like to teach the world to sing
in perfect harmony.
I stand more chance of doing that
than I do with my Year Three.

Fe fe fe fe fe fe fe fe fe...

Fi fi fi fi fi fi fi...

Fo fo fo fo fo fo fo fo fo...

FUM! Ha ha ha ha...

The Singing Singhs Sing Some Things

Mr Singh sings some sixteen things
Mrs Singh sings some sixty
Son Sammy Singh sings some seventy things
Sam's sister Sally seldom sleeps soundly.

La la la la la la la la...

Fa fa fa fa fa fa fa fa...

Me me me me me me me me me me...

Teenagers from Hell

Door slammers
Money scammers
Fast txtng
Party planners
Zit squeezers
Self pleasers
Non-verbal
Sigh heavers
Shop loving
Big spenders
Mirror gazing
Pretenders
Strop throwers
Hair growers
Any question
Dunnoers
Tale tellers
Bed dwellers
Whenever they see someone they fancy
Abuse yellers
Snide sniggers
Mine's biggers
Tonsil tickling
Wet kissers
Short-tempered
Fierce frowners
ALL UP or ...

... ALL DOWNERS

In bathrooms
Spend ages
Quite normal

Teenagers.

The Thingummywhatmagig

When I cannot find the right word
But another one won't do.
Or forget which number leaves me twelve
When multiplied by two.
If I can't put a face to someone's name
Or a name to someone's face
I use a *thingummywhatmagig*
Instead to take its place.

If you use a *thingummywhatmagig*
You'll probably go quite far
Though it's *thingummywhatmagig* easier
To simply just say
Blah!

Boys Are from Mars,
Girls Are from Venus

Girls are from Venus
Boys are from Mars
Yet they live side by side
On this planet of ours.

Both cry
If they bump themselves hard on the head
Both show an aversion
To going to bed
Both enjoy telly
Both are quite prone
To hate eating spinach
And being alone
Both like their birthday
Both love their cat
Both make a mess
And collect plastic tat
Both will chew pencils
Both harbour nits
They've plenty in common

That's about it!

The Price is Wrong

I want that branded T-shirt,
The logo-ed training shoes.
I want to have a thousand things
I'll hardly ever use.
I need the latest DVD,
I must have that new toy,
Those shorts, the sweatshirt and the watch
Will bring me endless joy.
Won't eat that other burger,
Must have the one which tastes
The same the whole world over
To stuff my greedy face.
I want a new school rucksack now!
The one so cool and chic
That it might go out of fashion
If I wait another week.

But my dreams are sewn in factories
By those who pay the price
Demanded by the global brands
To keep me looking nice.
My dreams are sewn in factories
For a pittance every day –
A miserable fraction
Of the price I finally pay.
So I'm not going to buy those brands no more
I'd find it hard to sleep
In a world where a T-shirt costs the earth
Yet a life is really cheap.

Do We Have to Kiss?

Do we have to Kiss?
Can't we just hold hands
Can't we both agree
To make other plans?
I might accidentally get your nose
Get the giggles
If I tread on your toes
A hand-shake won't do instead, I suppose?
Do we have to Kiss?

Do we have to Kiss?
Are we old enough
Do we need this wet, romantic stuff
Are you sure that you know what to do
Should I stand on your chair
Cos I'm shorter than you
Do we have to Kiss?

Do we have to Kiss?
Do you think it's true
That it gives you spots and gastric flu
Makes your jaw-bone ache
And your ears turn pink
Isn't it just like plunging
A blocked-up sink
Do we have to Kiss?

If we're going to Kiss
Better do it quick
The anticipation makes me sick
... It's not too bad
It's almost fun
Now slowly
Give me another one ...

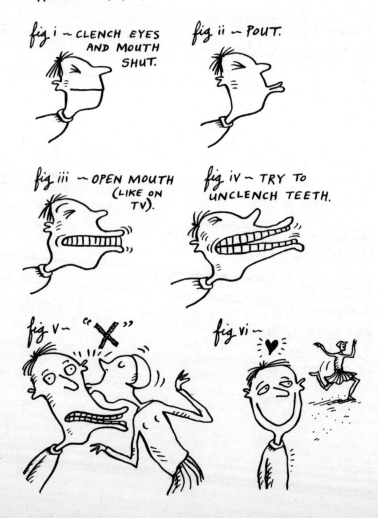

HOW TO KISS:

fig i ~ CLENCH EYES AND MOUTH SHUT.

fig ii ~ POUT.

fig iii ~ OPEN MOUTH (LIKE ON TV).

fig iv ~ TRY TO UNCLENCH TEETH.

fig v ~ "X"

fig vi ~ ♥

The Seven Deadly E-mails

Avarice *n. eager desire for wealth.*

To: Mr and Mrs Rice

From: Your Deserving Daughter Ava

Subject: Raising my Pocket Money

You're so mean.
All my friends get loads more than I do
It's not fair
It's really unfair
I DESERVE IT
My piggy bank is virtually empty
If it was a real pig
               it would have starved to death by now
Please can I have some more?
Big PLEASE
Pretty *please*
Pretty big *PLEASE*
Pretty big bold ***PLEASE***
Because I'm your favourite daughter
Because I'm your *only* daughter
Because you love me
Because I'm your **favourite**
                     only
                        daughter

Who you love **so** much
That if I fell under a bus tomorrow
You'd be sorry that you hadn't spoilt me today
Go on ... PLEEEEEEEZE
I promise I'll be good
For EVER and EVER
OK then, for a WEEK
All right, make that a DAY
Oh, let's be realistic: for about FIVE MINUTES
Which is five minutes more than nothing, isn't it?
That's a deal?

MORE, MORE, **MORE!!**

Five whole minutes of goodness for *you*
And loads more money for *me*
You are the nicest parents in the world
                              the galaxy
                                  the known universe
                                      the unknown universe

No I'm **not** just saying it
I really **mean** it
Why do you say – flattery won't get me anywhere?

I **want** it
I **need** it
I can't live **without** it
I'll **cry** if I can't have it
I'll **sulk** for a year
I'll never tidy my bedroom **ever** again
I'll **marry** someone you hate as soon as I turn sixteen
(Or is it eighteen? Whatever)
YOU JUST WAIT
Except that I probably won't live that long
Cos if you don't give it to me soon
I'LL DIE!

Just a *bit* more then
So that I can keep up with my friends
So that I don't get left out
So that people won't point at me in the street
     And whisper:
'There goes that *poor, poor* child,
The one with the really *mean* parents.'

I'll love you sooooo much if you do!
It'll ruin my life if you don't!
Just **think** about it, will you?
The last thing I want to do is put any
PRESSURE
on you.

This Won't Hurt a Bit

There will be times
When the stars won't seem like stars at all
But a million bombs about to fall.
When you're drowning, not walking
And the pavement is pulled from underneath your feet.
Your limbs become plasticine,
It feels that the gentlest breeze
Turns on you and throws you to the street.
When you long to run away
But someone forces you to sit
And listen to the lie that
This won't hurt a bit.

You will try smiling –
It freezes your jaw and teeth.
You will try putting on a brave face,
But a frightened one still lurks beneath.
You will try thinking of happier times
But only bad ones seem to come to mind,
Until you're left clinging to the lie
You've heard so often
It's become a fact:
This won't ... this won't hurt ...
This won't hurt a bit.

How many cruel untruths
Have adults told
Trying to pretend that pain does not exist?
And to whose benefit

Is the worn-out conceit
That being strong means never being weak?
The point is this:
Being alive means sometimes feeling pain.
You'll fall down countless times
But always get up again
And it might hurt a bit.

Autistic

You feel you cannot reach
                    me.
You feel that I'm
                adrift,
A small boat lost on your
Enormous sea.
But I *can* hear you,
                    just,
As sailors hear mermaids sing
On the edge of the horizon.
I can see you
                far away,
A coppery, spinning coin
Which slips between the inky ocean
And the darkening sky.
Wait.
I am busy
Studying this shell,
Remembering its shape
With my fingertips.
I am happy
Under its spell.

The Lost Word

I am on the tip of your tongue,
hidden in the creases of your memory.
I am disobedient,
I will not come when called.
I feel your jaw clench.
I tremble slightly
when you umm and urr
but I lurk just out of reach.

I am exactly what you need
to answer a question
or win an argument.
I lie curled in the dictionary
sound asleep.
You cannot find my starting letter
to begin your search.
I am most precious to you
when you fight to remember me.

Then, without warning,
days or hours later
I appear.
I pop into your head –
a snail's pace Superman
too late to save the world.
You're so surprised
you blurt me out.
That's it, you think
the word I wanted!
And everyone stares at you
like you've gone mad.
But for once they're listening
just to me,
loud and clear and strong.

Not part of a longer sentence
but me,
by myself
alone.
And I feel ...
          ... and I feel ...
                    ... I feel urr ...
                              ... feel umm ...
                                        ... urrrr ummm
                                        ...
You know ...
          ... really umm ...
                    ... really urr ...
Well ...
like *that* anyway.

Power Poetry

Can a poem
>   Feed the starving
>   Disarm a missile
>   Bring back the dead soldier
>   or the missing limb
>   Replace the smile of a child
>   who's lost his mum and dad

>   ?

Can it
>   Stop a bullet
>   Sweeten bitterness
>   Dry tears
>   Make us forget
>   everything spiteful
>   that was ever said

>   ?

Could it
>   Be used in hospitals when they run out of blood
>   Fill the fields with daisies rather than landmines
>   Make everyone suddenly burst out singing

>   ?

Might it
        Whisper in the ears of murderers
                    and generals
        Make leaders listen more than they talk
        Force deadly enemies
                    to step into each other's shoes
        and see through each other's eyes

Let the richest man on earth
                    know how it feels
        to live on nothing more each day than
                    a single bowl of rice

                    ?

Or does it
        simply
            tell
                another
                    story,

One
    with
        a
          happier
                ending

            ?

Being in a Bad Mood

... is a bit like being
stuck in a soggy anorak
with no arms, no zip
and a huge wet flapping hood
which sits on your head
like a tired-out seagull.
You know you've got
to pull yourself out of it
or else suffer
when the sun appears.

How to Be an Eccentric

Actually wear the clothes which elderly relatives
have given you for birthdays/Christmas, etc.

Quack rather than saying yes or no.

Always carry an open umbrella.

Eat sprouts. Eat more sprouts. Never say anything cruel
about sprouts ever again.

Pay the telephone bill out of your pocket money.

Tell your sister how beautiful she is.

Pull a perfectly sensible face in the school photograph.

How to Be Really Creepy

(See above)

Being Down in the Dumps

... is every bit as bad as it sounds
and a lot smellier.
Imagine being at the bottom
of a black plastic bin bag
which is full of old curry, limp salad
and bacon fat
on a sweltering day
and then multiply by a thousand
and add rats
and rolls of mouldy, wet carpet
and the terrible BEEP BEEP BEEP
of a huge reversing truck
that's come to dump another stinking load
on top of you.
It's enough to make anyone
feel a little gloomy.

This Way Up

A directionless lady from Louth
Kept putting her foot in her mouth
   But that was before
   Now it stays on the floor
Cos the weather is better down south.

Coughs and Sneezes Spread Diseases

Inconsiderate Baron Von HOFF
Never covered his mouth for a cough
   His enormous sneezes
   Spread snot and diseases
Till a giant one blew his head off.

Cheaters Never Prosper

A terrible loser, Sly Spain
Always cheated at every known game
   He didn't much care
   Till he played solitaire
When to win and to lose felt the same.

Gone with the Wind

A careless young girl, Prudence Whickers
Went to church without wearing some knickers
   She wasn't much fussed
   Then a sharp windy gust
Blew her skirt up in front of three vicars.

Mother Knows Best

SWELL...

Vain daughters are told by their mothers
That they're vastly superior to others
   Imagine how bad
   They feel when they hear Dad
Say exactly the same to their brothers.

POP!

Stay in Touch

A lazy teenager called Joan
Never bothered to pick up the phone
    So she missed out on dates
    Lost touch with her mates
And spent every evening alone.

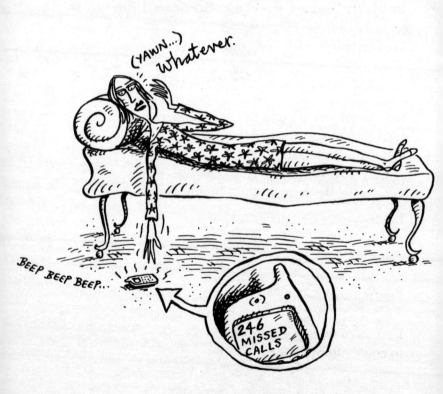

The Seven Deadly E-mails

Sloth *n.*   *laziness, sluggishness.*

To: The National Theatre

From: S. Loth

Subject: Getting dressed without all the effort

We came on a school trip the other day and saw backstage

I really liked meeting the lady who works as
a *dresser* for the actors.

As you only put on plays in the evening
I wonder if she would be free
to help me put my school uniform on in the morning.

I'm fed up being late for school
and my mum says I'm not a baby any more
and should do it myself.

I don't mind paying

I get £5 a week pocket money
so could afford about 25p a day

Tell her not to worry about weekends
I usually just keep my pyjamas on all day.

Only the Only

He's one in a million
The one and only
One of a kind
Alone not lonely

Always the favourite
Always the best
The one correct answer
In a one-question test

Not a third of a trio
Or half of a pair
The primest prime number
The only one there

The Plateful

I hate what's left on my plate.
What's left on my plate hates me.
We've been staring at each other now
Like two slow-motion gunslingers
For almost an hour.
We're getting colder and colder
Quieter and quieter
Not a knife or a fork makes a scrape.
Neither of us is allowed to leave the table
Until we've finished.
Everyone is in for a very long wait ...
. . . .
. . . .
... What's left on my plate hates me
And I hate what's left on my plate.

I Don't Want to Grow Up

I want to be THIS age
                    forever.
I never thought I would
                    say that
Because being the age I was LAST year
                                was so good.

And I remember wishing that I could
Have been THAT age
                    forever
If time had stood
                    still
Which it never will.
But even so
I think, I know
That I want to be THIS age
                    forever.
(If only it didn't mean missing my birthday.)

Why Old People Say the Things They Do When Young People Ask Them How They Are

Mustn't grumble
Can't complain
Not too bad, thanks
Much the same
Bright as a button
or the sun
Perky
I'm ninety-one years young!
Fit as a fiddle
Sharp as a knife
Never felt better
in all my life.
I'm glad you asked
But I'll keep it snappy
And briefly tell you
That I'm quite happy.
If I had more time
I'd tell you the truth
But I don't want to waste it
Like I did in my youth.

Be Careful What You Wish For

Clara was fed up with herself
And wished that she was someone else,
Something which people often do
But in Clara's case the wish came true.
The sky turned green, the grass turned blue
Clara changed into someone who
Didn't look at all like Clara did
Or did things which Clara liked to do:
Like watching telly with her mum;
Secretly sucking on her thumb;
Drinking Coke and eating beans;
Reading trashy magazines;
Having friends called Jade and Rose;
Tickling her sister's toes;
Taking the dog out for a walk;
Ringing Granny for a talk;
Pulling on her favourite jeans;
Dreaming happy Clara dreams.
Instead Someone Else lived a nightmare
About Clara – the girl who wasn't there:
Who didn't have the mum and dad
That lucky Clara once had had.
Nor did she have the good friends who
She'd had before her wish came true.

That's the end of Clara.
There is no more.
What remains is a moral
One shouldn't ignore:
'Be very careful
What you wish for!'

Imperfect

I am not perfect   My brown eyes hold conversations
with the stars

I am not perfect   I laugh and the birds stop singing
to listen

I am not perfect   My smile illuminates whole cities

I am not perfect   I have much work to do

Worst Sellers
(Books which I Probably Won't Write)

Do It Yourself Dentistry

How to Fail Every Test You'll Ever Take

Eat Yourself Fatter

The Lonely Chef – Recipes to Poison Your Friends

Caring for Your Nits

Ruin Your Life the Easy Way

The Queen – Fashion Icon and Foxy Chick

More Love Poems About a Bedside Lamp

100 Very Boring Places to Visit

Learn to Speak Spanish Really Badly in Just Eight Years

How to Make a Snail Fall in Love with You

KNIGHT IN
SHINING,
SILVER-
PAINTED
PLASTIC
ARMOUR.

Buy it a training shoe
Try not to rush things
Tell it how much you *hate* French food
Tickle its feelers
Feed it a bunch of flowers
Invite it to a cricket match
Pretend not to notice that it's three days late for every date
Write it an epic poem
Send it a copy of *Caravan and Motorhome Weekly*
Always hold doors open for it
Spend a cosy night in together watching paint dry
Avoid salty snacks before kissing it goodnight.

Index of First Lines

91

Choosing a brilliant book
can be a tricky business...
but not any more

www.puffin.co.uk

The best selection of books at your fingertips

So get clicking!

Searching the site is easy – you'll find
what you're looking for at the click of a mouse,
from great authors to brilliant books and more!

Psst!
What's happening?

sneakpreviews@puffin

For all the inside information on the hottest new books,

click on the Puffin

Read more in Puffin

For complete information about books available from Puffin – and Penguin – and how to order them, contact us at the appropriate address below. Please note that for copyright reasons the selection of books varies from country to country.

www.puffin.co.uk

In the United Kingdom: Please write to Dept EP, Penguin Books Ltd, Bath Road, Harmondsworth, West Drayton, Middlesex UB7 ODA

In the United States: Please write to Penguin Putnam Inc., P.O. Box 12289, Dept B, Newark, New Jersey 07101–5289 or call 1–800–788–6262

In Canada: Please write to Penguin Books Canada Ltd, 10 Alcorn Avenue, Suite 300, Toronto, Ontario M4V 3B2

In Australia: Please write to Penguin Books Australia Ltd, P.O. Box 257, Ringwood, Victoria 3134

In New Zealand: Please write to Penguin Books (NZ) Ltd, Private Bag 102902, North Shore Mail Centre, Auckland 10

In India: Please write to Penguin Books India Pvt Ltd, 11 Panscheel Shopping Centre, Panscheel Park, New Delhi 110 017

In the Netherlands: Please write to Penguin Books Netherlands bv, Postbus 3507, NL–1001 AH Amsterdam

In Germany: Please write to Penguin Books Deutschland GmbH, Metzlerstrasse 26, 60594 Frankfurt am Main

In Spain: Please write to Penguin Books S. A., Bravo Murillo 19, 1° B, 28015 Madrid

In Italy: Please write to Penguin Italia s.r.l., Via Felice Casati 20, I–20124 Milano

In France: Please write to Penguin France S. A., 17 rue Lejeune, F–31000 Toulouse

In Japan: Please write to Penguin Books Japan, Ishikiribashi Building, 2–5–4, Suido, Bunkyo-ku, Tokyo 112

In South Africa: Please write to Longman Penguin Southern Africa (Pty) Ltd, Private Bag X08, Bertsham 2013